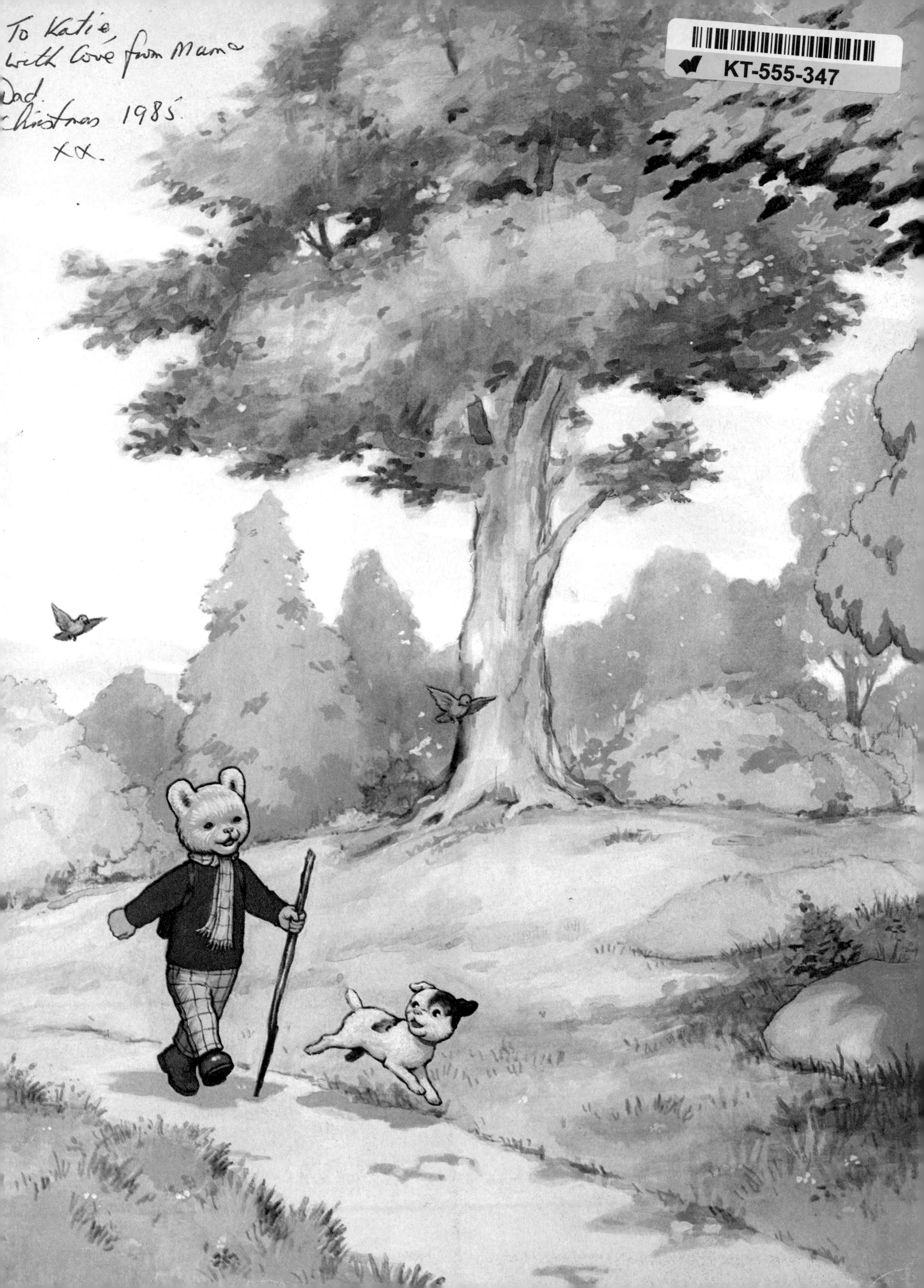

To Katie,
with Love from Mama
Dad.
Christmas 1985
xx.

50

This is the fiftieth Rupert Annual. Today's grandparents were young children when the first Rupert Annual appeared in 1936. All of that first annual was the work of one man, the artist Alfred Bestall who was to repeat that performance every year until 1973 when he gave up painting the covers and the famous endpapers, although his stories and drawings have continued to appear. In a way this fiftieth annual is a salute to him. On the back cover Rupert's party guests include a man with a sketchbook — Alfred Bestall.

For this special annual we have chosen a story from each of the six decades over which the Rupert Annual has been published. The first four are by Alfred Bestall. The remaining two are both by John Harrold and James Henderson. We believe these six stories show that Rupert is truly timeless and that half a century has not dimmed the magic of the little bear and the world of Nutwood.

RUPERT

CONTENTS

This Book Belongs To:

Katie Vicat.

ISBN 0 85079 154 5

£2.75

RUPERT, BILL

*While Rupert shops with Mr. Bear,
Along comes Bill, who cries, "Hey, there!"*

Rupert and Mr. Bear are shopping in the village when they are hailed by a familiar voice. Looking round, Rupert is pleased to see his old chum Bill Badger running after them.

Bill joins the shopping expedition and they meet a small boy with his guy. "Of course, it is the fifth of November today!" exclaims Mr. Bear. "We must buy some fireworks."

and the PEARLS

They meet a small boy with his guy;
"Some fireworks," Father says, "we'll buy."

While in the fireworks shop he notes,
How on that guy Bill Badger dotes.

Mr. Bear and Rupert are busy buying fireworks, but Bill gazes wistfully at the little boy's guy. Mr. Bear notices this and kindly suggests that they make a guy of their own.

Rupert and Bill eagerly agree and hurry back to Rupert's garden. Mr. Bear builds the bonfire, and Mrs. Bear provides a fine assortment of old clothes in which to dress the guy.

"We'll burn a guy," says Mr. Bear;
So in the garden they prepare.

BILL BEHAVES STRANGELY

Says Bill, "I'll come back after tea;
Oh, shan't we have a jolly spree?"

He watches, quiet as a mouse,
Until the Bears are in their house.

Now after tea Bill is so late
They can for him no longer wait.

They light the fire and strange to say
That guy begins to run away.

Proudly they place the finished guy on top of the bonfire in readiness for the evening's sport. They separate for tea and Bill promises to return directly it is dark.

But instead of going home, Bill hides behind the gate until Rupert and his father have entered the house. It is plain from his mysterious behaviour that Bill is planning some mischief.

Rupert and Mr. Bear wait for Bill, but time passes and he does not appear. Rupert is unwilling to start without his chum, but Mr. Bear declares they can wait no longer.

Mr. Bear strikes a match to set light to the bonfire and then an astonishing thing happens. Their seemingly harmless guy suddenly springs to life and dashes away across the garden.

RUPERT CHASES THE GUY

He tears off at a furious rate,
While Rupert follows through the gate.

"Oh, what a chance!" thinks little Bear,
"If only Bill were here to share!"

Beside a barn he goes to ground;
He's gone when Rupert comes around.

Then from the barn a figure queer
Cries "Whoop!" and Rupert falls with fear.

This most peculiar guy seems to know his way about the garden, for he heads straight for the open gate. Rupert is the first to recover and starts in hot pursuit.

Then follows a long and exciting chase over the downs. "This is a weird adventure," pants Rupert as he races along, "but I do wish Bill was here to share it."

The guy runs towards a farm and disappears round the corner of an outhouse. Rupert is only a few yards behind, but when he arrives the guy has completely disappeared.

Very puzzled, the little bear looks around for some trace of the guy. Suddenly, with a loud "Whoop," the strange figure springs from the window, giving poor Rupert another unpleasant surprise.

BILL REVEALS HIMSELF

"I'll take my mask off," says the guy;
"It's Bill," gasps Rupert with a sigh.

A man is coming down the hill;
"I'm going to startle him," says Bill.

Bill rushes at him with a jump,
And down fall all his parcels—bump!

"That's most unkind, Bill," Rupert cries;
"I'm going back to apologise."

Suddenly the guy removes its mask, revealing Bill's cheery face. "Ha-ha" he chuckles, "fancy you thinking the guy had come to life. I got into its clothes while you were at tea."

Bill is in a mischievous mood to-day and wishes to continue the game. "I will jump out at this man as he passes," he says, and hastily dons the disguise once again.

Just as the gentleman passes their hiding place, Bill jumps out with a yell. The poor old man is so startled that he drops all his parcels in the road.

Bill is highly delighted at the success of his joke, but Rupert is rather ashamed and tells Bill that he is going back to apologise and help pick up the parcels.

RUPERT AND BILL APOLOGISE

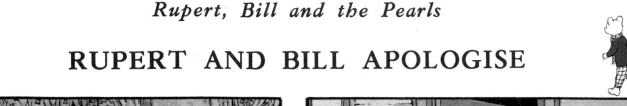

The man says, "If you're sorry, friends,
You'll help me home to make amends."

When home they have a nasty fright;
The door stands open; that's not right.

They find that burglars have been there,
And taken pearls of beauty rare.

Then Rupert says, "What can we do?
I know! We'll fetch the police for you."

The gentleman proves to be a sport and laughs heartily at the joke. "Now," he says, "perhaps you will show you are really sorry by helping me carry all my parcels home."

Rupert and Bill readily agree. As they approach the house their companion stops and exclaims "Why, the door is open! I'm certain I closed it when I went out this morning."

All is chaos in the house. The old man rushes to his strong-box and finds it open. "They have taken all my silver and a valuable pearl necklace," he groans.

"Can't you 'phone for help?" suggests Bill, but there is no telephone near. Rupert has a better plan. "Bill and I will go for a policeman, we can run faster than you."

THEY RUN FOR HELP

The friends set out upon their way,
But mist comes, causing them delay.

It thickens, and the gallant pair
Are lost, and nearly in despair.

Says Bill, "That man might know the way;"
But he has not a word to say.

"Why, it's an ivy-covered oak!"
Says Rupert—Bill laughs, "What a joke!"

Rupert and Bill race from the house determined to recover the silver and pearls. To make their task more difficult a mist appears and they are forced to slacken speed.

In a short while the mist thickens into a real November fog and the chums realise with a shock that they are completely lost. How unfamiliar everything looks in the gloom.

"Let's ask the man the way," says Bill, pointing to a dim figure in the fog. They call out several times, but to their surprise the man appears not to hear.

"That's funny!" exclaims Rupert, "I wonder if he is deaf?" Cautiously they approach the figure and find they have been shouting at an old ivy-covered tree trunk. "What a joke," chuckles Bill.

THE CAT ADVISES THEM

Into a pool they almost slide;
It's near where young Bill went to hide.

The barn cat says, with wisdom true,
"If you're lost, then the thief's lost, too."

But while he shows them bedding soft,
They hear some footsteps in the loft.

A shadow passes, so the cat
Says, "Strange! I must see into that."

The chums wander on and very nearly fall into a pond. "Why, Bill," says Rupert excitedly, "isn't this near the barn where you hid?" "Yes, it is just over here," agrees Bill.

A cat is sitting in the window and Rupert explains their trouble. "If you cannot find your way in the fog, neither can the thief," he says wisely. "Come inside and rest."

The cat leads the way into the barn, and tells Rupert and Bill to make themselves comfortable with straw and blankets. Suddenly they hear footsteps in the loft above.

A dim form moves past the window. "That's not my master," whispers the cat, "that man is a stranger, and we must go and see what he has been doing."

To search the loft the three decide
And Puss goes first to act as guide.

They see a bulky-looking sack,
And think they're on the burglar's track.

Yes! Pearls and silverware are there;
Says Rupert, "Bad man! How he dare!"

The thief outside hears voices high,
And says, "I'll see, who's come to spy?"

When they think the man is well away, they creep outside and find a ladder against the wall. The cat runs up to the loft, Rupert and Bill following close behind.

They discover a sack on the floor, and the cat exclaims in surprise, "This does not belong to my master! That stranger must have left it here." "Let's open it," suggests Rupert.

To their amazement, the sack contains valuable silverware and a beautiful pearl necklace. Rupert gasps as he realises they have found the articles stolen from their friend, the old man.

But in their excitement, Rupert and Bill have made too much noise and given away their presence to the thief. He quietly returns and begins to climb the ladder to the loft.

THEY PREPARE FOR A SIEGE

Then Rupert hears, and with a bound
He flings the burglar to the ground.

And while he bars the door inside
Bill bravely tries the sack to hide.

Then Rupert, turning from the door
Sees Bill and sack crash through the floor.

Bill lands unhurt on coverings soft,
But Rupert stays up in the loft.

Rupert hears the thief in the nick of time, and runs to the loft door. He is just able to push the ladder aside and the thief falls to the ground.

Bill and the cat drag the precious sack to a safer hiding place while Rupert hurriedly bars the door. He wonders if they will have to spend the night in the loft.

Rupert turns to help Bill, but before he can reach him there is a loud crash. A piece of the flooring has given way, and Bill, the cat, and the sack disappear.

Luckily they fall on the sacks below and are not hurt. Rupert, guessing that the thief has heard the crash, thrusts the valuable pearls into his pocket and remains in the loft.

THE CAPTURE OF BILL

The noise has made the thief turn back,
And now on Bill he makes attack.

Bill's tucked beneath the burglar's arm;
Poor Rupert follows in alarm.

Though thick the fog, he daren't delay,
So chooses the most likely way.

He hunts, and cries, "Where can *he* be?"
Then sleeps, exhausted, near a tree.

Rupert is right. The man enters the barn and finds Bill with the sack. "You come along with me," he snaps. "Perhaps this will teach you not to interfere again."

He shoulders the sack and with Bill under his arm leaves the barn. Meanwhile Rupert has found a length of rope in the loft, and quickly descends to follow his chum.

The fog is now so dense that Rupert, although only a few yards behind, cannot see the thief. Knowing he must not delay, he sets off in the most likely direction.

For a long while the little bear wanders on until he is completely lost. At length, tired out, he lies down on the leaves under a tree, and is soon fast asleep.

RUPERT FINDS A FRIEND

When Rupert wakes to daylight clear,
A gipsy boy is standing near.

He says, on hearing Rupert's tale,
"Let's ask my Gran—her help won't fail."

"Thieves used to meet near here," says Gran;
"We'll find their haunts, dears, if we can."

So after breakfast off they go,
And Granny leads, with footsteps slow.

Rupert awakes to find the fog has cleared. A gipsy boy is standing near and he tells Rupert his name is Rollo. "Is anything wrong?" he asks kindly.

He seems so anxious to help that Rupert tells him about the thief and Bill. "Come and see my Granny," suggests Rollo. "She is very wise and may be able to help you."

The old gipsy listens carefully to Rupert's story. "There was once a secret meeting place for thieves near here," she says slowly. "After breakfast we will go and look for it."

Rupert is very excited when they start out for their search on the moors. "It's many years since I came this way," says Rollo's granny, "but I think this is right."

RUPERT HEARS BILL

At length she says, "The spot's just there;"
Cries Rupert, "Hark! Bill's voice somewhere!"

He puts his ear down to a stone;
Bill's calling in a frightened tone.

"Let's lift the stone," says Rupert, "Oh!
A hole and ladder are below!"

Then Rupert says, "This hole defend,
While I go down to find my friend."

The old gipsy pauses and says, "I think this is the spot." Suddenly Rupert holds up his hand for silence and cries excitedly, "I can hear Bill's voice coming from somewhere."

They listen attentively and the sound appears to come from under their feet. Rupert puts his ear to a large stone. Yes, he can plainly hear his chum calling for help.

Rupert and Rollo manage to move the heavy stone and reveal a deep hole. An iron ladder runs down one side and Rupert says he is going to look for Bill.

Rollo wishes to go down as well, but Rupert thinks he had better keep watch above. The descent is made more difficult as the rungs of the ladder are slippery with moss.

RUPERT REACHES THE CAVE

He climbs down quickly, full of fear;
Bill's voice he can no longer hear.

Down steps he runs with all his might
And at the end he sees a light.

And Bill lies there upon the ground,
With cruel ropes all tightly bound.

"The thief will make a get-away,"
Says Bill, "if here we longer stay."

At the bottom of the ladder Rupert finds a flight of steps leading through a dark tunnel. He grows anxious as he hurries along, for he can no longer hear Bill calling.

In a few minutes he sees a beam of light coming from a cave at the end of the tunnel. Rupert approaches cautiously—perhaps the thief is in the cave.

When Rupert first enters the cave he thinks it is empty, and then he sees poor Bill tied to the ground. Bill is amazed to see Rupert in this secret hiding place.

While Rupert unties the cord Bill explains that the thief intends to get away with the silver when the fog clears. "But it has cleared!" exclaims Rupert. "We must follow at once."

THEY FIND THE THIEF

They hurry to the tunnel's end,
They there the rugged rocks ascend.

Close by the thief, with treasure, stands,
And watches while an airplane lands.

Then in the 'plane the sack is packed;
Says Rupert, "We must quickly act."

Bill runs for help while Rupert tries
To catch the 'plane before it flies.

Rupert and Bill hurry along and soon reach the end of the tunnel. They find a large hole in the roof and by climbing the rocks manage to scramble out into daylight.

They are very surprised to see the thief standing nearby and are afraid he may have heard them. But he is anxiously watching an airplane and does not notice their approach.

As the airplane lands, the thief runs up and hands the sack of stolen silver to the pilot. The chums realise they must act quickly if they are to prevent their escape.

Bill goes for help and Rupert chases after the airplane with the wild idea of clinging to the under-carriage. The airplane is gathering speed, but he is just able to reach it.

RUPERT'S THRILLING RIDE

Bill stops a cyclist on the road,
And tells what's in the airplane stowed.

Poor Rupert's nearly blown away,
It's such a very windy day.

The cyclist says, "A 'plane we'll need,
So to my brother we must speed."

"My 'plane," the brother says, "I'll lend,"
And off they go to help Bill's friend.

Bill reaches the main road just in time to stop a motor cyclist. He briefly explains what has happened and points to the airplane, where they can see Rupert clinging on.

Meanwhile the little bear is finding his perch very blowy. He has difficulty in holding on against the wind from the propeller. "My word," he gasps, "I shall be glad to land."

The man with the motor cycle is energetic. "There isn't time to fetch the police," he shouts. "My brother owns a plane. Jump up behind me and we will ask him to help."

The brother eagerly agrees to the adventure and shortly they are speeding in the direction they judge the thieves have taken. Bill is certainly fortunate to have found such helpful friends.

THE AIRPLANE LANDS

For miles, with cold poor Rupert's numb;
Then down the 'plane begins to come.

With heavy bumps it strikes the ground,
And Rupert, thrown, rolls round and round.

Unhurt, he hides behind a tree,
The actions of the thieves to see.

He steals up, quiet as a mouse,
And sees the men climb in a house.

The thieves continue their flight for many miles and poor Rupert is numb with cold and very exhausted. He is wondering how long he can hold on when the airplane begins to descend.

The airplane lands and at the first bump on the ground Rupert is thrown off. Fortunately he rolls clear and, apart from being shaken, is little the worse for his experience.

Rupert soon recovers, and realising that the men do not know he is there, hides behind a tree. The thieves take the sack of silver from the airplane and run for cover.

They make for an empty house and go round to the back, where they enter through an open window. Rupert follows as closely as possible, determined not to lose sight of them.

THEY DISCOVER THEIR LOSS

For him the window's far too high;
And so he finds a log near by.

Watching, he hears the pilot say,
"Without the pearls you've come away."

Poor Rupert slips, and to the ground
He falls, while both men look around.

Then through the window leaps the thief,
And little Rupert comes to grief.

The men disappear into the house and Rupert runs up to follow. The window is too high for him, but he finds a log near by and manages to roll it into position.

As Rupert peeps through the window, the pilot discovers the pearls are missing. "You must have left them in the cave or the barn," he shouts angrily. "We must return at once."

Rupert is watching with such interest that his foot slips on the log and he falls to the ground with a thud. The men turn round just in time to see him disappearing.

The little bear quickly scrambles to his feet and dashes away from the house, but one of the thieves is already through the window, and poor Rupert is soon captured.

Rupert, Bill and the Pearls

THE THIEVES DEPART

The thieves say, "Now we'll stop your tricks!"
And lock him up—Oh! what a fix!

To find the necklace off they go;
That Rupert has it they don't know.

A 'plane by Rupert's window flies,
To summon it he bravely tries.

"This glass," he says, "reflects sun's rays,
I'll focus them, and make a blaze."

The thieves are furious with Rupert for interfering, and he is carried to the top of the house and locked in a tumble-down attic. "This will stop your tricks," chuckles the man.

They start out to look for the pearls, and then it is Rupert's turn to chuckle as he pulls the beautiful necklace from his pocket. "I think I've won this time," he says.

Rupert's attention is suddenly attracted by a loud humming, and looking out of the window he sees an airplane flying low, near the house. Quickly he thrusts the pearls into his pocket.

Seeing an old cracked mirror on the floor of the attic, Rupert has the idea of attracting the attention of the occupants of the airplane by reflecting the rays of the sun.

BILL FINDS HIS CHUM

The blaze of light Bill's first to see;
He cries, "What can that signal be?"

The cyclist says, "I see your friend;
There's something wrong, we must descend."

They haven't got the attic key,
So force the door, and Rupert's free.

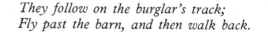

They follow on the burglar's track;
Fly past the barn, and then walk back.

The pilot is turning in pursuit of the thieves' airplane when Bill sees a flash of light from the mirror. "That looks like a signal," he cries excitedly. "Who can it be?"

Bill's companion looks through his field glasses and sees the little bear at the window, waving frantically for them to stop. "It is your chum. We must land and see what is wrong."

Bill and the brothers who are helping him land and easily force the door of the attic. "Hurry," cries Rupert, "and we shall catch them with the stolen goods at the barn."

They are soon speeding back to the barn and there, sure enough, is the thieves' airplane in the field below. They land a short distance away and cautiously make their way back.

THEY PLAN A TRAP

"They talked," cries Puss, "of some trap-door."
Says Rupert, "I've seen that before."

A boulder to the spot they roll,
To shut the thieves up in a hole.

One brother stays to guard the door,
The rest set off across the moor.

The tunnel entrance there they find;
The pilot says, "This end I'll mind."

Their friend the cat tells them that the men have been in and gone again. "They spoke of a trap-door," he adds. "Oh! We know where that is," cry the chums.

Yes, the trap-door is open and they can hear voices below. The men bring a boulder near in readiness to block the entrance and trap the thieves in their underground lair.

"Now for the entrance on the moors," says Rupert. One of the men stays to keep guard and the others set out to search for the spot the old gipsy found.

When they reach the entrance they hear footsteps coming along the tunnel. Their friend sends Rupert and Bill for assistance and says grimly, "I'll see they don't escape this time."

RUPERT SPRINGS A SURPRISE

The pair, though tired, run with haste
To show the burglars' hiding place.

The burglars know they're caught at last,
So to the police their sack they cast.

"My pearls!" the owner cries in grief;
"They're gone for ever," sneers a thief.

Then Rupert from his pocket whirls,
To their surprise, the string of pearls.

Luckily the two chums find Mr. Bear and a policeman who are out looking for Rupert and Bill. They round up the old gentleman and set out across the moors again.

They find their friend still on watch. And now that the thieves realise there is no chance of escape they heave out their sack of loot and give themselves up. They are astounded to see Rupert.

Suddenly the old gentleman who is examining his belongings cries out in horror. "Oh, my pearls are missing!" "You'll never see those again," sneers one thief. "They're lost for ever."

But Rupert has one last surprise in store for them. "No," he chuckles, "they are not lost." To the amazement of everyone he pulls the beautiful necklace out of his pocket.

RUPERT and PONG-PING'S PARTY

1940s

The odd things that happened to Rupert and Podgy when they went to see one of Pong-Ping's Christmas presents

RUPERT GETS AN INVITATION

*"Oh, Postman!" Rupert calls, "I see
You have a letter there for me."*

*It's from Pong-Ping, who wants to know
If Rupert to his house may go.*

*When Rupert sets out on the day,
He meets his chum along the way.*

*They both are puzzled by one thing,
So straight away they ask Pong-Ping.*

Christmas is near and Rupert is keeping a sharp look-out for the postman. To-day he is lucky, there is a letter for him. "It's from Pong-Ping, Daddy," he says. "He's inviting me to a party and he says he wants to show me a Christmas present that somebody has lent him." "That sounds rather odd," murmurs Mr. Bear. "People generally *give* presents, not lend them. I wonder what he means." "If I can go to the party I can come back and tell you," laughs Rupert.

On the day of the party Rupert sets out and before long he sees Podgy Pig also plodding through the snow. "Hullo, Rupert," cries the little pig. "Are you coming to Pong-Ping's party? Tell me, did you notice anything queer in the invitation that he sent you?" Rupert smiles as he runs to join him. "Yes, I couldn't understand one of the words," he says. Soon the little Peke is welcoming them at his front door. "Do tell us," says Podgy, "has someone really *lent* you a present?"

RUPERT SEES THE CARPET

The Peke then tells them that he meant,
This gift, for just one day, is lent.

He takes them to a room quite bare,
But says, "You'll find my present there."

"Well," Rupert cries, "what can it be?
There's nothing here that I can see."

"It's on the floor!" the Peke replies;
"I said I had a big surprise."

Pong-Ping chuckles. "In my part of China people don't always give presents," he explains. "If they own something very precious they sometimes lend it for a time. My friend, the old Mandarin has lent me something very wonderful, so it's all mine, but only for one day. Come, I'll show it you." He flings open a door and Rupert and Podgy gaze around. There are some lanterns hanging up but there is no furniture, not even a chair or a table, and nothing that looks at all like a Christmas present.

"You're making fun of us," declares Podgy. "There's no present here unless you mean one of the lanterns." "You're not very sharp to-day," laughs Pong-Ping. "Well," says Rupert, "there's only one other thing in the room at all, and that's the little carpet!" He bends over it. "This can't be it," he murmurs. "It's a bit grubby and nearly threadbare." "All the same, that *is* it," says the little Peke. "The Mandarin has lent it me for a whole day and it's the most wonderful carpet in all the world!"

RUPERT TAKES A RIDE

He's waiting now for one more guest,
Before he will explain the rest.

They hope that Margot won't be long,
It seems that something has gone wrong.

Kind Pong-Ping feels quite worried now,
And wishes he could help somehow.

As soon as Pong-Ping says, "I wish . . ."
The carpet rises with a swish.

Rupert is very puzzled. He bends down to look more closely at the carpet. "You'll understand soon," says Pong-Ping, "as soon as our party is complete. I only invited three of you because there's only room for four people to sit comfortably on the carpet." "Who was the other person?" asks Rupert. "It was your friend Margot," says the little Peke, "I can't imagine why she hasn't turned up. She's very late." Taking the two pals into another room he gazes out over the snow.

"Did you say we had to *sit* on the carpet?" asks Rupert. "Let's try." "It's not very comfy, is it?" grunts Podgy, when they have gone back. But Pong-Ping is worried. "I wish we could see what has happened to Margot," he says absent-mindedly. No sooner has he spoken than an amazing thing happens. The carpet rises as if they were all as light as feathers, whisks them backwards through the doorway, into the other room and straight out of the window which is still open.

RUPERT FINDS MARGOT

Straight from the house the carpet flies,
Then sails, quite smoothly, through the skies.

When suddenly it comes down low,
They see poor Margot in the snow.

The carpet sets them down just near,
And Margot calls, "I'm glad you're here."

They find it hard to move about,
But soon they have her safely out.

Rupert and Podgy are too astonished to move as the carpet carries them up into the air. "I should have told you," gasps Pong-Ping, "this is a magic carpet. Each person who gets on to it may have one wish, and only one. I spoke without thinking, so I've had my wish and I can't have another!" To Rupert's relief the carpet doesn't wobble but sails steadily onwards and then begins to descend. "Look, there's someone stuck in the snow," he cries. "I do believe it's Margot herself!"

The magic carpet settles gently on the snow and Pong-Ping stares at Margot. "What ever are you doing here? And why didn't you come to my party?" he asks. "I tried to take a short cut and I sank into this snowdrift," she says, with her teeth chattering. "I've struggled and struggled but I can't get out." Rupert and Podgy at once go to help her. They, too, sink in the soft, powdery whiteness, but they manage to hoist her on to the carpet and then lift themselves up after her.

RUPERT HEARS PODGY'S WISH

Now Podgy wishes for the sun,
And quite forgets what he has done.

The carpet leaves the ground once more,
Exactly as it did before.

'Oh dear!' gasps Podgy in dismay,
"I wished that we were far away."

The magic carpet goes so fast,
They leave the land behind at last.

Margot is bewildered at the sudden appearance of the little pals, so Pong-Ping starts to tell her about the fun he had meant them to have at his house with the Mandarin's carpet. Meanwhile, Podgy and Rupert are shivering. "If only we'd been able to bring our overcoats," murmurs Podgy, "I wish we were somewhere a bit warmer." Instantly the carpet rises and carries them rapidly over the hedges and away up into the sky. Podgy topples forward while Margot calls out and clings to Pong-Ping.

Finding the carpet keeps steady, Margot gets less frightened but Pong-Ping is very annoyed. "What's all this?" he demands. "Has anybody wished a wish?" "Yes, I did," says Podgy, trembling. "I forgot what would happen. I was terribly cold and I said I wished we were in a warmer place, and then this thing whisked us off." "Well it can't be helped now, but I do wonder where we're going," says Rupert, as the carpet glides faster and faster to the coast, over the cliffs and then out to sea.

RUPERT FINDS AN ISLAND

A dreadful storm fills them with fright,
But they come safely through all right.

They see, as gently down they go,
Some tiny islands there below.

The carpet settles on the ground,
And Rupert runs to look around.

There are some strange things to be seen,
But little Pong-Ping is not keen.

Now that there is no land underneath them the little friends feel less safe than ever. "Look, there's an awful storm ahead," says Rupert. "Whatever will happen?" But to their amazement nothing seems to affect the carpet at all. Although the wind howls and under the driving rain the waves seethe and crash, they sail straight through without being touched. Beyond the storm is a smooth sea dotted with islands. "It's warmer already," says Podgy, "and I do believe we're coming down."

The magic carpet settles smoothly on one of the larger islands and the friends cautiously look around. "Oh dear, this isn't a bit what I meant to happen when I invited you all to my party," says Pong-Ping. "Let's be very careful how we make our next wish so that we go straight back again." But Rupert and Podgy are interested. "This is a wonderful island," says the little bear. "Look what lovely things are growing here. Do let's have a walk here before we start for home!"

32

RUPERT SEES THE VILLAGE

When snakes appear behind a rock,
It gives the chums a nasty shock.

They turn and run without delay,
Until they are quite far away.

"My goodness!" gasps the little bear,
"Those men look very cross down there!"

Once more they run, and soon they reach
The others waiting on the beach.

Pong-Ping and Margot decide to stay near the magic carpet. "I must keep an eye on it," says the little Peke. "It's only mine for one day and I mustn't risk losing it, so don't be long." Rupert and Podgy stroll away and gaze at the palm trees and the highly-coloured plants. "This is a grand place. I wish I lived here," says Podgy. But he changes his mind suddenly when three great snakes appear over a slope. The two friends turn and run. "They're not following," whispers Rupert.

Wanting to avoid the snakes, Rupert and Podgy take another way back to the carpet. Reaching the top of a small hill, they get a shock, for below them is a little village of round huts and, while they watch, a man spies them. He shouts angrily and others dash out of the huts. "My! They don't seem to like strangers!" gasps Rupert. "Come on! Run!" Soon Pong-Ping and Margot come in sight. "Phew! This is too hot for running," puffs Podgy. "I'd rather be back in the snow."

RUPERT SEES A STRANGE LAND

"Oh do be quick!" they cry in fear,
"We've got to get away from here."

The islanders come crowding round,
But, just in time, they leave the ground.

They long to be at home again,
But they are far away, that's plain.

Now Pong-Ping points far down below,
"The Mandarin lives there, I know!"

When he reaches the others Podgy flops down out of breath, but Rupert points. "Quick, we must get away," he gasps. "Some men are after us. And they don't like outsiders!" "On to the carpet all of you!" cries Pong-Ping. "Oh dear, I wish this old carpet would go home," sighs Margot. She is only just in time. At the moment the islanders arrive the carpet rises. They leap and grab and shout, but the four pals are out of reach and heading for the sea.

The friends sigh with relief as the island disappears behind them. "Now we'll soon be home," says Rupert. "But those great mountains don't look much like England, do they?" The carpet sails over the heights and strange buildings appear beneath. "I see what's happened," cries Pong-Ping suddenly. "We've gone wrong again. Margot said she wished the carpet would go home. Well, it's done so. But it isn't our home. It's the home of the carpet! Look, there's the Mandarin's house!"

RUPERT MAKES THE LAST WISH

Straight to the house the carpet flies,
And settles there, to their surprise.

"There's my wish left," says Rupert Bear,
Then wishes with the greatest care.

Again they start their magic flight,
And trust they will get home all right.

Three flying dragons now appear,
But are unable to get near.

No sooner has Pong-Ping spoken than the carpet floats down and settles in the courtyard of a great Chinese house. Rupert looks very worried. "D'you know, we're nearly in a fix," he says. "We only get one wish each and I'm the only one who hasn't had one. If my wish goes wrong, as yours have done, we may never get home at all!" Then, making the others take their places on the carpet, he says very slowly and carefully, "I want to go to a real Christmas Party at Pong-Ping's house."

At Rupert's words the carpet rises obediently for the last time and floats steadily away. But Pong-Ping looks doubtful. "I don't think even you will get your wish," he says. "I didn't prepare a real Christmas party but only a little one so that I could show you three this carpet." "Well, we'll wait and see," says Rupert. As they cross the mountains three flying dragons appear, but the great creatures cannot keep up with the speed of the carpet and are soon left far behind.

RUPERT HAS A REAL PARTY

When Nutwood comes in sight, they see
A really lovely Christmas tree.

They wonder who has left it there,
Then for the party they prepare.

To Pong-Ping's house goes everything,
The carpet, last of all, they bring.

So now they talk of all they've done,
And think that it was lots of fun.

When their own village again comes in sight, the four friends stare in delight, for on a slope near Pong-Ping's house is a small Christmas tree full of presents and lots of packages of sweets, fruit, cakes, puddings and crackers, all lying in the snow. The carpet alights and they run to the good things. "Your wish has proved how magic the carpet is, Rupert," cries Pong-Ping, "I didn't expect any of these things. Come on, let's take them all into my house and have a real Christmas party!"

The last thing to be brought in is the carpet. "We've none of us got any wishes left, so we shan't want this again," laughs Pong-Ping. Then they all put on paper caps and spread out the good things. "So far, yours has been the oddest party I've ever been at. We've been all over the world!" cries Rupert. "Yes," says the little Peke, "and I've just noticed another thing that shows how very, very magic that carpet is. Look at the clock. All those travels have only taken us half an hour!"

This is the design painted by Alfred Bestall for the dust-jacket (the loose cover) of the first Rupert Annual in 1936 which is the book Rupert is carrying on the cover of this, the fiftieth, Rupert Annual

RUPERT and the UNKNOWN

RUPERT HEARS A STRANGE NOISE

"What's that I hear?" asks Rupert Bear,
"It seems to come from over there."

Soon he hears a muttering sound,
And finds an old man on the ground.

Rupert is strolling home one sunny morning, after playing with his pals, when he pauses beside an old oak tree and listens. "What's that noise I can hear?" he murmurs. "It's different from anything I have ever heard before." Sure enough, a loud crackling noise is coming from behind the tree. "I must find out what it is," he says and, climbing over the fence, he gazes round to see what he can discover. By this time the crackling noise has ceased, and instead Rupert can hear someone muttering. He tip-toes forward and peers round a bush, and to his astonishment he sees a little old man sitting on the ground. The stranger is quaintly dressed in a thick coat and heavy boots and there is something rather odd about him that puzzles the little bear. Rupert runs to help the man, who is holding his head.

JOURNEY

1950s

RUPERT HELPS A LITTLE MAN

Says Rupert, "Oh, he's very small,
Not like a grown-up man at all!"

He helps the dizzy man along,
To Mrs. Bear, who says, "What's wrong?"

Rupert asks the man what has happened and if he needs help, but the little stranger stares at him with a frown and does not seem to understand. With Rupert's help he manages to stagger to his feet. "Why, he's hardly any taller than I am!" Rupert thinks. "How did he get here? What's the matter with him?" Once more the little bear questions the manikin, who mumbles one or two words in reply. "I think he's speaking in a foreign language," thinks Rupert. Then he beckons the stranger. "Perhaps you'll feel better after a cup of tea," he says. "I'll take you home with me." The little man is still very dazed and rests heavily on Rupert's shoulder as he allows himself to be led to the Bears' cottage. "Why, who *have* you brought this time?" gasps Mrs. Bear as the couple enter. "Is he a new friend of yours?"

RUPERT FINDS A PUZZLING THING

"What made that noise? I'll go and see!"
Says Rupert, standing near the tree.

A sudden crackling sound nearby
Makes startled Rupert leap up high.

"This thing, which gave me such a fright,
Is metal, but it's very light."

"I can't examine it down here,
So first of all, I'll pull it clear."

Rupert tells Mrs. Bear how he found the manikin. "I've no idea where he came from," he says, "and he doesn't seem to speak English. If you'll take care of him for a bit, I'll go back to that strange sound." As he reaches the tree there is another short burst of noise and the whole air shakes. Climbing the fence again, Rupert pushes through long grass. He jumps in alarm as a sudden loud crackling comes from a metal knob almost under his feet. Then the noise stops abruptly. "What was that thing?" gasps Rupert. Making his way carefully, he peers under the leaves where a queer-looking object meets his eyes. Very gingerly he touches it, then pushes it. "Why, it's quite light and it's metal too," he says. The noise has stopped, so he slowly pulls the object free and looks at it. "But what on earth is it?" he thinks.

RUPERT IS WHISKED AWAY

Says Ferdy to the little pup,
"It's turned itself the right way up!"

"What's this thing for? I can't decide,"
Thinks Rupert, as he steps inside.

"It's off the ground! I didn't know!"
Gasps Rupert, gazing down below.

The strange craft flies away so high,
They lose it in the cloudy sky.

Some of Rupert's pals, seeing him dragging the queer thing out of the bush, run forward. Before they reach him they pause and stare, for, although the little bear is not touching it, the strange cigar-shaped thing rolls slowly over until the mast is upright. "Goodness, it's hollow!" exclaims Rupert. "It would hold me." Inquisitively he creeps forward and after hesitating he steps inside—and at that moment a violent crackling starts again. Rupert is so intent on gazing at the metal knob at the top of the mast that is now sending out furious crackles, that he doesn't notice what is happening until he peeps over the side of the cockpit. Then he gets a shock, for the ground is now far below him. While his pals look on helplessly, the metal thing that is holding the little bear rises higher and higher and soon disappears.

RUPERT HAS A SWIFT JOURNEY

Then over sea and mountain-top,
The airship flies without a stop.

"I cannot steer this thing! Oh dear!
It's sure to hit the wall, I fear!"

The knobs meet with a dazzling flash,
And so the airship doesn't crash.

The manikins all stand and stare
When they catch sight of Rupert Bear.

Rupert finds himself unable to move or think after the extraordinary thing that has happened. The metal object gathers speed and streaks through the upper air at a tremendous rate over seas and mountains. "This must be a sort of airship," he thinks, "but how does it keep up? My, it's cold up here!" At length a grim-looking castle appears right ahead. "Oh, oh! We're going to hit it!" he gasps, closing his eyes tightly.

But to Rupert's relief the tiny airship does not hit the building. There is a vivid flash as the metal knob connects with another attached to a tower, and Rupert is left swinging helplessly. Next moment some small figures come out and, catching sight of the little bear, they stare in blank astonishment. "Why, they're just like the man I met at Nutwood," murmurs Rupert. "Can this be his home?"

RUPERT MEETS A MAN IN BLACK

Thinks Rupert, *"Well, there's not much doubt
That these men think I should get out!"*

*"It's all an accident you know,
I didn't mean to make it go!"*

*"It's really not my fault, you see,"
Says Rupert, "don't be cross with me!"*

*The man does not reply himself,
But takes some books down from the shelf.*

At length the small people move. One of them turns off a switch and two others lift the metal thing to the terrace so that Rupert can get out. "Please, I didn't mean to make this thing go," he quavers. "Is it yours? I know I oughtn't to have been inquisitive. And please, where am I?" The manikins only gather round and gaze at him. "Oh dear, perhaps they don't understand a word I'm saying!" he sighs. "This is going to be so awkward!" Before he knows what is happening, Rupert is hustled to another tower and confronted by another manikin dressed all in black, who seems to be the person in charge. "Oh, please don't frown at me," says the little bear. He tells the whole story and the other, making no reply, takes a couple of large books from a shelf. "What is he looking for?" thinks Rupert.

RUPERT SEES HIS VILLAGE

The man in black then starts to look
Through all the pages of a book.

Though Rupert can't tell what they say,
He watches as the men obey.

But soon the frame is filled with light,
And then his journey comes in sight.

Then, turning round in great surprise,
"This place is Nutwood!" Rupert cries.

Still in complete silence the chief manikin studies one of the books. "Why, I can see the word 'England'," Rupert mutters. "He must have understood what I was telling him." Before he can speak again the chief strides out, and shouts orders in a strange language to the other manikins who scatter in all directions, then he hurries Rupert into an inner room. There, the head manikin places Rupert before a large frame and begins to work complicated machinery. The frame fills with light and, as Rupert watches, lovely views appear on it, showing mountains, sea and forest. "That's the sort of place I flew over on the way here," he says. "It's just like going on a journey back! And, look—there's my very own village, Nutwood!" He turns, and at his cry, the manikin chief goes to another set of switches.

RUPERT WEARS SPECIAL CLOTHES

He wants to stay and see some more,
But he is taken to a store.

"Is this my coat?" asks Rupert, "Good!
I do feel warm with this big hood!"

The little people gather round,
And soon the ship is skyward bound.

"We're off!" cries Rupert Bear, "Hooray!"
And then the airship streaks away.

Things now happen quickly. Rupert is led away from the chief manikin, who still hasn't said a word to him, and is taken through tunnels and down stairs until his guide reaches a store. From it he brings him a heavy duffle coat with a huge hood, thick gloves and long boots to pull on over his own. Then a dark-haired manikin, similarly dressed, appears. "They're both smiling at me," thinks Rupert, "the first smiles I've seen here." The little bear soon sees why the thick clothes have been given to him. Without waiting an instant he is bustled outside and lifted into the tiny airship. His new friend squeezes in with him while other manikins crowd round. Suddenly the crackling starts again, and the little craft rises until the metal knobs connect again. Then with a loud fizzing noise the airship streaks away with its two passengers.

RUPERT LANDS NEAR HOME

And faster, faster through the sky,
The little man and Rupert fly.

Then as they land on Nutwood's height,
The other airman comes in sight.

The flier greets his friend with joy,
And hugs him like a little boy.

But just then, running up the hill,
Comes Ferdy Fox along with Bill.

Even faster than on the outward journey, the weird airship whizzes over forest, mountain and sea on the same route. At length it slackens speed and drops gently towards a hill. Rupert gives a happy shout. "This is my own village! See, there's the church." His companion pays no attention but is already settling the ship on the grass. "Good gracious! Look who's coming!" cries Rupert, as they both climb out. "It's the lost manikin!" When the two manikins catch sight of each other they rush together joyfully. Then, forgetting all about Rupert, they dash back up the slope to the airship. "Well, of all the extraordinary people!" says the little bear. "They must be terribly brainy and they all look old and bald, yet they scuttle about like schoolboys!" Turning, he sees some of his friends who want to know what has happened.

RUPERT SHOWS HIS OUTFIT

"Where have you been to all the day?
Do tell us, Rupert, please!" they say.

"Well, if I knew, I'd tell you so!
But honestly, I just don't know!"

"That little man was very queer,
And now he's gone away, I fear!"

"I like those clothes they gave to you,"
Says Bill, "I wish I had some too!"

Before the pals can reach the top of the slope, however, the queer craft has shot away. "Now Rupert," demands Ferdy Fox, "what was that thing, and where have you been?" Rupert stares at him and then he bursts out laughing. "I haven't the least idea!" he cries. "I couldn't understand a word anybody said, and no one told me where I was or how I got there, so I don't know anything at all!" Mrs. Bear is waiting for Rupert as he reaches the cottage. "That visitor you brought!" she says. "He wouldn't talk and he wouldn't eat. Suddenly he heard a loud crackling noise and rushed out of the cottage." "I thought as much," Rupert smiles. "Don't worry! He's happy now and they've forgotten all about us—but do look at this topping flying suit they've given me after my unknown journey!"

RUPERT

and the SNOWSTORM

1960s

RUPERT IS SENT FOR MEDICINE

"Poor Daddy does have such a cold.
So fetch his medicine," Rupert's told.

With snuffles, sneezes and a cough,
He says, "Just let me sleep it off."

A bitter wind begins to blow.
It's really cold enough for snow.

For colds in either head or chest
It seems this medicine is the best.

November has just about come to an end and the weather has turned wild. "Come here, dear," Mrs. Bear calls to Rupert. "Put on your coat and scarf and run to the shop for Daddy's medicine. It's such bad luck that he should have caught so bad a cold with Christmas coming on." Mr. Bear wheezes grumpily, "Oh, medicine's no good. Just let me sleep it off." Rupert looks at him anxiously then, taking his own small shopping carrier, he sets off.

"Poor Daddy," thinks Rupert as he starts across the common. "He sounds quite ill. My, isn't it cold! What a wind! And now it's starting to sleet. I don't like this." However, he soon reaches the chemist's shop safely only to realise that Mummy hasn't told him what medicine to get. But when he explains what is wrong with Mr. Bear the chemist says, "Ah, yes. I know what he needs." He hands over a packet. "This is the best medicine I know," he says.

RUPERT IS CAUGHT IN A STORM

The sleet has stopped but in its stead
A great dark cloud looms overhead.

Rupert takes shelter in the lee
Of a broad and sturdy old tree.

But that protection does not last.
He's swept off by the icy blast.

Then all at once the storm moves on,
The sky is clear, the wind has gone.

The sleet storm has stopped by the time Rupert sets out for home. But before many minutes a change in the light makes him glance nervously at the sky. "Look at that cloud!" he gasps. "It really is as black as ink. Whatever am I in for?" He soon finds out as a violent blast of wind suddenly buffets him and a moment later a blinding snowstorm swirls about him. Desperately he stumbles towards a broad old tree and cowers against its trunk with his back to the storm.

With every second the storm seems to get fiercer. Then just when it seems it can get no worse a sudden shift of the wind snatches Rupert from his shelter and tumbles him over and over for what seems like ages. Through it all he keeps hold of his carrier. Then as suddenly as it came the storm is gone. The wind has dropped. The air is clear. But the whole landscape is now covered with a thick carpet of snow. On hands and knees Rupert stares after the storm cloud.

RUPERT MEETS TIGERLILY

He can't believe his eyes. He blinks.
The cloud has stopped and now it shrinks.

"That's Tigerlily!" Rupert cries.
To tell her of the cloud he flies.

He's so het up he doesn't look,
So doesn't see an icy brook.

The little girl, with twinkling eyes,
Says paddling now's not very wise.

Rupert rises unsteadily and watches wide-eyed the very strange behaviour of the storm cloud. It settles over a tall building among trees then starts to get smaller and smaller until it disappears. The building is one Rupert knows well. It is the pagoda home of the Chinese Conjurer and his daughter Tigerlily, one of Rupert's friends. "I must tell them about this," Rupert says aloud and hurries towards the pagoda. As he gets near it Tigerlily appears from the trees and comes to meet him. Rupert is so anxious to tell her what he has seen that he doesn't notice a brook covered with thin ice. Crack! And in he goes! "Hey, what you do, Rupert?" cries Tigerlily. "Why so much hurry?" Then she giggles. "And it is not wise to paddle at this time of year. You surely catch cold!" Rupert stares at her. "Don't be silly, Tigerlily!" he says through chattering teeth. "You don't think I did this on purpose?"

RUPERT HEARS OF THE SORCERER

He tells her what he's come about
As Tigerlily helps him out.

"That's not a storm!" she laughs aloud.
"Daddy's wise friend rides in that cloud."

"Do come indoors. You must be cold.
There I'll explain," Rupert is told.

"Our friend rides storm to travel here,
And then he makes it disappear."

As Tigerlily helps him from the icy water Rupert says, "I was coming to tell you about the strange snowstorm." He can hardly speak for shivering. "It settled over your house and then just disappeared." Poor Rupert, he can hardly believe his eyes when Tigerlily leans back against a tree and bursts out laughing. "Oh, dear!" she chuckles. "You do not understand. That not a real snowstorm. My Daddy's friend the Sorcerer has come to visit us." Before

Rupert can say that he doesn't understand and that it jolly well looked like a snowstorm to him, Tigerlily takes his hand and hustles him indoors to get warm. As they hang up their coats she says, "I explain. The Sorcerer is powerful magician. He used to travel in flying saucer. But now he rides in snowstorm so nobody can see him. Snowstorm very swift. You notice? Then as soon as he gets where he is going he makes his snowstorm disappear. Very clever."

RUPERT MEETS THE SORCERER

Says Tigerlily, "My friend here
Has had an accident, I fear."

When Rupert's brought in to explain,
The Conjurer says, "You again?"

The Sorcerer hears Rupert tell
Of how he chased the storm and fell.

The Sorcerer holds up a boot
And ponders what course would best suit.

Now Tigerlily leads the way along a corridor and stops at a door. Before knocking on it she whispers, "Sorcerer has come to see my Daddy about important new magic." Then she knocks, opens the door, bows and says, "Honourable Daddy, honourable guest, may we enter? I bring my friend Rupert. He is in trouble." "What, again?" the Conjurer says and next moment Rupert finds himself facing the Conjurer and another man, dressed in long brightly coloured robes and stern-looking.

Politely the Conjurer asks Rupert to explain his trouble. So he tells of his errand and about the snowstorm, ending, "Then it settled on this house and I ran after it to try and find out what it was all about and I fell through some ice . . ." "Say no more!" Gruffly the Sorcerer stops him. "Feet wet, yes? Then remove boots." Timidly Rupert does as he is told. The Sorcerer rises and for a long moment stands holding one of Rupert's boots. Both men begin to smile.

RUPERT HAS TO JUMP ABOUT

The man casts powder on the mat
And orders Rupert, "Jump on that."

Then sparkling stars and "flames" leap out.
How Rupert has to jump about!

At last when he can dance no more
Poor Rupert sinks down on the floor.

What looked like flames have done no harm
And now his feet are nice and warm.

Rupert begins to feel uncomfortable. The smiles of the two men are, well, mysterious. He sits watching on a chair. "Boots can wait," says the Sorcerer at last and tosses a handful of powder on the floor. "First, tootsie magic! You like to jump? Then jump on that!" Cautiously, Rupert obeys. Immediately sparks, stars and flames leap up all around him. Really frightened now, he jumps and jumps, higher and higher. But no matter how hard he tries or how high he jumps he cannot escape. Yet the flames and the rest look so alarming that he daren't stop. At last, though, he can go on no longer and he sinks to the floor exhausted. And nothing happens. "I—I'm not even scorched!" he gasps in amazement. He jumps up excitedly and turns to the Sorcerer. "That was wonderful!" he cries. "The flames didn't hurt at all. My feet were frozen and now they are really warm and dry." The Sorcerer smiles. "That magic never fails," he says.

*"Do dry my boots so that I may
With Daddy's stuff be on my way."*

*Although for feet the "flames" worked well,
For boots he'll need another spell.*

*Another spell they soon are shown.
A bag starts bouncing on its own.*

*It stops and from it floats a pair
Of boots to suit a little bear.*

Rupert is much happier now. "Oh, please," he begs the Sorcerer, "dry my boots in the same way. Then I can go home with my Daddy's medicine." There is a slight smile on the Sorcerer's face again as he looks silently at Rupert. "Boots take longer," he says quietly. "Must find something else. That needs big magic." Then he strides about the room muttering strange words and waving a wand. Tigerlily and Rupert look nervously about, waiting for something to happen.

Suddenly Rupert points. "Look!" he breathes. "That bag in the corner. It's moving." The two edge cautiously towards it. "Sorcerer bring this bag with him," Tigerlily whispers. "Maybe it is full of magic." Rupert starts as the bag begins to jiggle and bounce without anyone touching it. At last, with a sort of quiver, it settles on the floor. It opens and from it, very gently, two objects float. "Boots!" Rupert gasps. "Nice warm winter ones."

RUPERT GETS NEW BOOTS

Smiling, the Sorcerer says, "Lo!
Warm boots for you. Now home you go."

Above the floor the strange boots skim.
Where Rupert goes they follow him.

Timidly the boots he tries.
They're cumfy, warm and just his size.

Rupert recalls how all this while
The wise man hasn't ceased to smile.

Rupert can't take his eyes off the boots as they rise from the Sorcerer's bag and begin to float about the room. They drift slowly towards the Sorcerer and gently circle near his wand. Now the tall strange man is smiling broadly. "Little bear," he says, "put them on and go home." "Oh, I daren't," quavers Rupert. "Not if they're full of magic." He starts to back away from the boots but they march after him. "Don't be afraid," Tigerlily tells him. "They very nice and cumfy."

So Rupert screws up his courage. He stretches out one foot then the other and the boots slide on by themselves. Tigerlily is right. They are cumfy. Next moment Rupert is marching proudly about the room. "They're a perfect fit, too," he announces. "Now you can go home," says the Sorcerer. "All set now." When he speaks he smiles again in that mysterious way. As Rupert leaves he asks Tigerlily, "Is he really giving me these in exchange for my old pair?"

RUPERT'S BOOTS TAKE CONTROL

He wonders, are the boots on loan
Or have they swapped them for his own?

Now Rupert moves at such a rate.
The hard bit is just keeping straight.

He can't go straight, yet cannot stop.
The boots rush on, they skip and hop.

These are his own tracks Rupert's found.
He can't stop running round and round.

Tigerlily's answer does not leave Rupert any wiser. "Sorcerer say nothing about exchange," she murmurs. "Maybe you get your own boots when dry. Now hurry home." So Rupert sets off but as he goes he wonders why Tigerlily too was smiling a little smile. Oh, well, he has the new boots for the moment anyway and they really are beautifully warm and comfortable. What's more—and this is strange—he can run over the snow faster than he could in his old boots.

But, what's this? The boots seem to want to go their own way. They keep swerving away from the path Rupert wants to take. Desperately Rupert tries to head for home but the boots just won't let him. "Oh, this is awful!" he cries. "What do they want me to do?" Just then he spies footprints ahead of him. He stares. "They're mine!" he gasps. "These wretched boots are making me run in circles. And I can't stop! Oh, dear I shall be worn out soon."

RUPERT CAN'T STOP RUNNING

He tries so hard to break away,
But, no, the weird boots make him stay.

"I can't go on like this!" he cries,
Kicks off the boots and sideways flies.

He props himself against a tree
And thinks, "Thank goodness now I'm free."

But round the tree the boots still go
Trampling a circle in the snow.

Round and round Rupert goes. Soon the track is so trampled that no single footprint can be seen. And still he can't break away. "This is impossible," he gasps. "I can't go on like this. There's only one thing to do. But can I do it?" With a mighty effort he throws himself sideways and drags his feet from the boots. He lands heavily in the soft snow at the foot of a tree. "Whew!" he breathes. "What a relief! I thought I was done for there." He sits up and leans against the tree. "I'm exhausted," he groans. "I wonder how often I went round before I managed to break away." As he gets his breath back Rupert realises he is becoming very uncomfortable again. "My poor feet," he shivers. "They're absolutely frozen. I must be moving on. My toes aren't going to like trudging through the snow in just socks." He rises to go and stops in astonishment. The boots are racing round the tree on their own. And faster than ever too.

RUPERT'S FRIEND TURNS UP

Still on and on the boots race round,
Then Rupert hears a welcome sound.

It's Tigerlily—smiling too!
She laughs and says, "The joke's on you."

She says, "The Sorcerer played such
A trick because you asked too much."

So long as those boots ring about
The tree poor Rupert can't get out.

Rupert is standing looking uncertainly at the circling boots when he hears a cheery "Cooee!" He looks up to see Tigerlily approaching. "I say, look what's happened!" he calls. "Those boots just won't stop. They keep going round and round this track." He tries to cross the track to reach Tigerlily and catches his breath. "I—I can't get over the track," he gasps. He tries again in vain. Tigerlily only smiles. "I expect this," she says. "No harm done. Just Sorcerer's joke." Rupert stares. "Joke!" he repeats. "I don't think it's funny. My poor feet are freezing." "Oh, yes, very funny," Tigerlily giggles. "You see, Sorcerer wanted to teach you a lesson for being too curious about snowstorm so he give you magic boots. They make magic circle and you not able get out. Oh, yes, very funny!" "But what am I to do?" wails Rupert. "The boots keep running round and round. I can't stay here for ever, now can I?"

RUPERT IS SET FREE

The broom she has is just the thing,
It seems, to break the magic ring.

Where Tigerlily sweeps the snow
The strange boots can no longer go.

The boots are safe now, Rupert's told.
He's glad. His feet are freezing cold.

His shopping satchel up he picks
And sets off hoping, "No more tricks!"

Tigerlily is too good a chum to go on laughing at Rupert's plight—even if she does think it is funny. "Not to worry," she says. "Daddy's magic broom soon set you free. Magic circle need magic broom. Watch!" She waits until the boots pass her then starts to sweep the track as hard as she can go. By the time the boots come round again she has swept a patch clear of snow. When the boots reach it they stop with a jerk then settle gently on the grass. Tigerlily gives a little smile: "There! Magic circle broken and trouble ends. Now boots are quite safe I promise." Gratefully Rupert pulls the boots onto his poor cold feet. "Ooh, lovely!" he says. "My feet are quite warm again right away." Then after a moment he adds, "But I hope the Sorcerer isn't going to play any more jokes. He has an odd idea of what's funny." Tigerlily, smiling happily, tells him he ought to hurry home. So Rupert picks up his carrier and hurries away.

RUPERT MAKES A DISCOVERY

An anxious Mummy's waiting when
Rupert at last gets home again.

"Whose are the boots? They aren't yours,"
Says Mrs. Bear when they're indoors.

"They're magical boots, or they were,"
Rupert explains to Mrs. Bear.

As Mr. Bear the boots is shown,
Young Rupert gives a little moan.

Mrs. Bear has been watching anxiously for Rupert and she is at the door as he runs up the path. "What a time you have been!" she says. "Did you get caught in that snowstorm? And what have you got on your feet? Those aren't your boots!" "I should think not!" laughs Rupert. "How I got them is a strange tale. I hope Daddy's no worse for his long wait. I say, these boots are warm. I'll be glad to get them off." As he removes them Mrs. Bear examines the boots. "Have you borrowed them from someone?" she asks. "Yes, I had to," Rupert tells her. "They're magic . . . at least they were." And he tells Mrs. Bear about the Sorcerer and the magic circle. As he speaks Mrs. Bear gets more and more concerned. "I think we should show them to Daddy," she decides. "And while we are about it you can give him the medicine you went for." So the boots are taken for Mr. Bear to see and Rupert dips into his carrier for the medicine. He gasps. The medicine has gone!

RUPERT CAN'T FIND THE BOOTS

The medicine's gone! He stands dismayed.
Meanwhile the boots to dry are laid.

Yet Mr. Bear is far from cross
And jokes about the medicine's loss.

But Mummy says, "You'll have to go
And find the medicine in the snow."

"The boots have gone. How very strange.
I'm sure they were here by the range."

While Rupert stares with dismay into his empty carrier Mrs. Bear bustles off with the boots to put them to dry by the kitchen range. "Oh, this is awful!" Rupert thinks. "Where can I have lost the medicine?" As soon as Mrs. Bear returns Rupert tells her about the loss. To his surprise his Daddy bursts out laughing. "Told you I didn't want the stuff," he guffaws. "I've no faith at all in medicines. After all the trouble you've had you've gone and lost it!" Mrs. Bear, though, does not think it is funny. "I must have lost it when I threw myself out of the boots," says Rupert. Mrs. Bear sighs. "Well," she says, "the Sorcerer has your boots so you must put on those furry ones again and go back to look for the medicine." "I'll go now," Rupert says and he goes into the kitchen to fetch the boots. But he can't see them anywhere. He gazes around and scratches his head. "Funny," he thinks. "I was sure Mummy said they were by the range."

RUPERT GETS A SHOCK

Then suddenly the boots leap out
To caper, jump and dance about.

When Rupert dashes off to tell
About the boots they come as well.

Alarmed, Rupert and Mrs. Bear
Cringe as the boots dance in the air.

The two boots want to go outside.
Rupert opens the window wide.

"The boots must be in here somewhere," Rupert murmurs. "I saw Mummy take them in. I'll have a search." But he doesn't have to look long, for as he approaches a broom in a corner the boots spring from behind it and rattle against a cupboard door. "Mummy!" he calls. "The boots have gone all magic again!" He backs out of the kitchen but the boots follow. "I can't put them on now," he cries. "I daren't even touch them. Why have they started acting like this again?"

Mrs. Bear is quite as nervous of the boots as Rupert is. The pair of them back away from boots which float higher and higher until they are at eye-level. "They're worse than when the Sorcerer first showed them to me!" gasps Rupert. The boots now float into another room and kick gently at a window. "I'm sure they want to get out," Rupert whispers. He screws up his courage, advances on the boots and throws open the window. To his great relief, out they fly.

RUPERT'S CHUM RE-APPEARS

*"You've no boots now," says Mummy, "so
To find the medicine I must go."*

*As Mrs. Bear puts on her hat
There comes a knock. Now who is that?*

*"It's Tigerlily!" Rupert gasps.
The little girl a large bag clasps.*

*Says Mrs. Bear, "Do stay and play,
But I must now be on my way."*

With the magic boots out of the way Rupert suddenly realises that now he has no boots. He sinks onto a footrest and says glumly, "So now I can't go out and look for Daddy's medicine. What *are* we to do?" Mrs. Bear sighs and then says, "It is quite clear I must go myself. Now, where are my outdoor shoes? And my thick coat? Here they are. Now, where do you think you dropped the medicine?" She is putting on her hat when there is a knock at the door. Rupert goes to open it and there on the doorstep is Tigerlily and she is smiling broadly. "Come in, my dear," Mrs. Bear greets her. "You can stay and play with Rupert but I'm afraid I must go out. You see, Rupert has no boots to wear . . ." "No, please, I think I can help," Tigerlily interrupts. "The Sorcerer sends me to say he enjoyed joke very much, very funny, and he says all well now and not to worry any more." She gives another big smile. But Rupert does not smile back.

RUPERT GETS HIS BOOTS BACK

"The Sorcerer has had his fun.
All's well," she says. "The joke is done."

The magic boots, she knows, have flown
And in their place here are his own.

It's good to have them back, and more,
They're better than they were before.

He's off to find the medicine when
What he hears makes him pause again.

"Do you mean to say your Sorcerer still thinks he's being funny?" Rupert bursts out. "First he jolly nearly froze me in a magic circle. Now he has my boots and his have flown away!" "Please, not to be cross," pleads Tigerlily. "Sorcerer is very clever. He calls back his own boots and in exchange—well, see what I bring." With that she opens the bag she is carrying and takes out two objects. "My own boots!" Rupert cries. "Oh, thank you, Tigerlily!" Happily he puts them on

and struts up and down. "You know, they are even more comfortable than they were before!" he exclaims. "Like I tell you," Tigerlily laughs. "Sorcerer very clever. If he makes jokes he makes very funny jokes. If he wants to make things better he makes them very better." She turns away and Rupert runs to get his overcoat. "Now I can go and search for the medicine and save Mummy the trouble," he thinks. But as he is going out he hears something that makes him pause.

RUPERT'S DADDY IS CURED

The little Chinese girl has brought,
It seems, whatever Mummy's got.

What's in the phial Mummy holds
Is best by far for coughs and colds.

Mr. Bear, sounding still quite gruff,
Supposes he must try the stuff.

His voice is now clear as a bell.
He says he's never felt so well.

It is a snatch of conversation that has made Rupert stop. He turns back to the sitting room where his Mummy has just taken a small phial from Tigerlily. "I don't understand," Mrs. Bear says sinking into a chair. "Explain it to me again, please." "Well," says Tigerlily, "Rupert told Sorcerer he has medicine for his Daddy who is sick. After Rupert leave, Sorcerer say he has medicine better than any shop. This is it. I give it to him now, please, so he will be cured quick." Mrs. Bear agrees but warns Tigerlily that Mr. Bear is rather grumpy. Tigerlily puts on her biggest smile and goes up to Rupert's Daddy holding out the phial. "Dear me, not more medicine!" grumbles Mr. Bear. "I thought I was free of the stuff when Rupert lost his lot. Oh, well, can't say no to a lady." And with that he takes a sip. Then a mouthful. Then he gets up, throws aside his rug and stares at the phial. "Amazing!" he cries. "I've never felt better!"

RUPERT MEETS THE STORM AGAIN

Now Mummy thinks the little bear
Should go and thank the Sorcerer.

Rupert says he is glad to find
The Sorcerer is really kind.

As Tigerlily's home they spy
A dark cloud rolls across the sky.

Why, as they flee before the cloud,
Does Tigerlily laugh aloud?

When Mr. Bear, singing in a clear voice, goes to smarten himself up the others are convinced the Sorcerer's medicine really has worked. Rupert is delighted and asks Tigerlily to thank the Sorcerer. "Maybe you should thank him yourself," Mrs. Bear tells Rupert. "His magic boots didn't harm us, your boots are better than ever and he has cured Daddy too." So Rupert puts on his coat again and soon Tigerlily and he are making their way over the snow to her Daddy's house.

As they reach the high ground overlooking the Conjurer's house Rupert asks, "Do you think your Daddy and the Sorcerer will have finished their discussion about magic. We won't be interrupting them again, will we?" Tigerlily doesn't reply. Instead she gives a gasp and exclaims, "Quick, back to the cottage! Not to stop! Not to wait!" And she turns and scampers back the way they have just come. Rupert is bewildered, especially by the fact that Tigerlily is laughing.

RUPERT WANTS NO MORE JOKES

And as they shelter from the blast
She laughs until the storm is past.

The little girl tells Mrs. Bear
The Sorcerer's no longer there.

"He travels in that storm of snow,"
She tells them as they watch it go.

"I do hope," Rupert laughs, "that he
Won't play another joke on me!"

Rupert discovers what they are running from when a snowstorm, more violent than ever, hits them and forces them to shelter. Still the little Chinese girl chuckles and beams. "I like this!" she says. "You see what happens? Very funny?" But before Rupert can say, no, he doesn't understand, the storm disappears, out comes the sun again and Tigerlily scampers off again towards Nutwood. Mrs. Bear greets them as they arrive. "My, have you thanked the Sorcerer already?" she asks. "Not possible!" Tigerlily replies. "Sorcerer gone again." Seeing that Mrs. Bear is puzzled she points to the dwindling storm and says, "Sorcerer is riding in that." But Mrs. Bear still isn't clear and over tea she asks, "Will every sudden snowstorm be your Sorcerer?" Tigerlily shrugs and says, "He used to ride in flying saucer. He change to this. Maybe he change again." "Well, just so long as he plays no more tricks on me," laughs Rupert.

HOW TO MAKE A PAPER BIRD

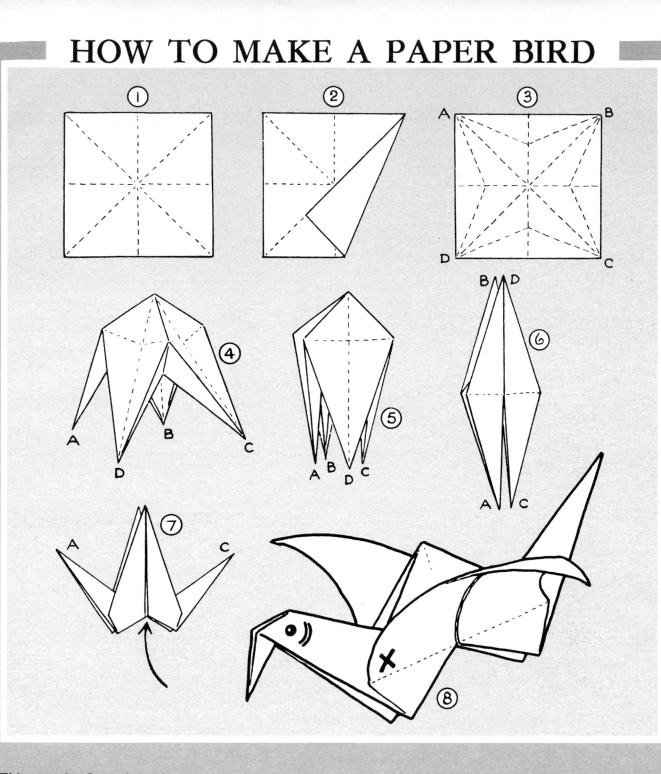

This was the first of the famous Paperfolds to appear in the Rupert Annual. That was in 1946 when the Paper Bird played an important part in a story called Rupert and the Magic Dart. To make it you start with a perfectly square piece of paper and fold it from corner to corner each way. Then turn it over and fold it from side to side as in (1). Next lay each side against a middle line (2) but press the fold only halfway along from the corner. Do this all round until the pattern of the folds looks like (3). Now turn the paper over again and press the four side panels under and, working by the folds you have made, gently bring the corners together as in (4) and (5). When A, B, C and D are tight together press everything firmly into its new position. Lift the opposing flaps B and D. These will be the wings (6). Now a tricky bit as you lift A and C to a halfway position as in (7). You reverse their folds to do this. The folds at the arrowed point must be neat and not torn. Fold down the tip of A to form the beak, draw in an eye then bend each wing gently into a curve as in (8). This is necessary to make the bird "work". To flap the wings hold the bird at X and gently pull its tail.

RUPERT and

The Bears have come to Rocky Bay
To spend their summer holiday.

It is the first day of Rupert's summer holiday at Rocky Bay and while his parents unpack he explores his favourite seaside town just to be sure everything is as he remembers it. Yes, all the familiar things are there . . . and one familiar sight he doesn't expect. Making his way busily along the front is the little servant of Rupert's old Nutwood friend, the Professor. At Rupert's shout of recognition the servant swings round.

John Harrold

*Now something strange makes Rupert stare.
The Old Professor's servant's there.*

*"Hey, stop a moment!" Rupert cries.
"This really is a nice surprise!"*

When he sees who has called he smiles. "I say, are you on holiday here?" pants Rupert when he catches up. "And is the Professor here with you?" The servant looks mysterious. "Yes, the Professor is here too," he says. "But we're not exactly on holiday." "Then what . . .?" Rupert begins. The servant holds up a hand. "I shall have to ask my master if I may tell you," he says. "Meet me here tomorrow after breakfast."

*The servant says, "I may make clear
Tomorrow what we're doing here."*

RUPERT MEETS HIS OLD FRIEND

Next morning Rupert finds he's led
Up to a towering sea-cliff head.

The servant says, "Down here we go
To meet my master far below."

And there upon a rocky ledge
His friend waits by the water's edge.

"Beneath that cover over there,
My new invention, little bear!"

Next day the servant is waiting for Rupert. The Professor, he says, agrees that Rupert may know what he is doing in Rocky Bay. "So follow me!" the servant cries and sets off at a brisk trot. Rupert has to run hard to keep up with him as they leave the town and head for the cliff tops. In fact, he is beginning to think he can't run much further when the servant stops beside a bush on the cliff edge. He pushes his way through it to reveal steps going down to the sea far below. He skips down the steep steps with Rupert at his heels. On a ledge at the bottom the Professor is waiting. "I forgot you'd be on holiday here," he greets Rupert. "Still, now you're here I'd better show you what I'm doing." He leads Rupert into a cave. Inside it is like a big sea pool. Around the pool are tools and work-benches. "There!" the Professor announces and points to a covered shape at the top of a ramp into the water. "My secret!"

RUPERT HEARS ABOUT SPIES

"Although it looks like other boats
This vessel flies as well as floats."

Then Rupert learns to his surprise
His friend is here to hide from spies.

Now Rupert sees at closer range
Indeed his friend's boat does look strange.

The Professor says Rupert may
Sail in his flying boat next day.

Rupert holds his breath as his friend tugs at the sheet covering the shape. But when the "secret" is revealed Rupert feels let down. It looks like an ordinary boat with furled sails. The Professor sees Rupert's disappointment. "It flies too!" he chuckles. When Rupert is over his astonishment he asks, "But why hide away here to build it?" The Professor turns serious. He says, "We began work in Rocky Bay then we found two suspicious looking boys lurking about the boatyard. Spying, I'm sure. So we moved to this cave which makes a wonderful workshop." Who the boys were he has no idea, he admits. Then he cheers up again and insists that Rupert sees the boat in the water. It is let down the ramp and the servant scrambles aboard. Rupert can see now that it has two masts side by side in front and three together at the back. Later as he is leaving the Professor calls, "Come again tomorrow and have a trip in it!"

Back to the cave his way he makes.
Two strange boys note the way he takes.

He looks around when at the brim
But can see no one watching him.

Spies and the like he quite forgets
As out to sea the vessel sets

A button's pressed, a strap snaps round
To keep young Rupert safe and sound.

Next morning—with Mummy's permission—Rupert scampers up to the cliff tops on his way to the Professor's cave and the promised trip in the new craft. But as he trots along he begins to feel that he is being followed, and once when he swings round suddenly he thinks he sees two shapes ducking behind some bushes. When he reaches the secret steps leading to the cave he pauses and looks around but there is no one to be seen and so down he goes.

In the excitement of the trip ahead Rupert forgets about his suspicions. The boat is already in the water and Rupert scrambles into the seat beside the Professor who is seated at the steering wheel. In a moment they are heading out with all sails set. "Before we take off just press that button on your seat," the Professor says. Rupert does so and a safety belt springs out and snaps into position. "Now away we go!" laughs the Professor.

RUPERT GOES FLYING

Now Rupert sees that those tall things
That look like sails are also wings

Sails spread like wings, now off they go!
And soon the sea lies far below.

The sea-birds falter in their flight
Quite startled by this strange new sight.

Up from the waves two dolphins rise.
The poor things can't believe their eyes.

The boat gathers speed. The Professor pushes a button and the front sails spread to form wings. The sails behind open out like the tail of an aircraft. Another button is pushed. "That starts the air propeller," the Professor says. And at that moment the boat lifts clear of the water and rises into the sky. "Oh, this is so exciting!" exclaims Rupert. At the same time he is jolly glad of the stout safety belt as he looks down at the sea a long way below.

Astonished gulls squawk as the boat suddenly appears among them. Then the Professor turns the wheel a little and pushes it forward. The boat swoops in a steep turn towards the waves. Rupert gasps as the sea seems to rush up at them. Then the Professor pulls back the wheel and the boat climbs again but not before a pair of dolphins have been left gasping in surprise. "Now," says the Professor, "would you like to fly the boat for a while?"

RUPERT TAKES THE WHEEL

It's Rupert's turn to have a go.
He takes the wheel—and down they go!

Despite the boat's upside-down flight
The special seats remain upright.

The old man says, "Let me explain."
And soon they're right-way-up again.

The Professor says, "I can't see
My servant waiting there for me."

When the boat is level and steady again Rupert and the Professor change places. The Professor is just saying, "It's really quite simple..." when Rupert pushes the wheel forward and the boat zooms into a steep dive. "Pull it back!" cries the Professor. Rupert does, but so hard that next moment the craft is upside down. Yet oddly enough Rupert and his friend are still right way up. "Aha! My special gyro-chairs," chuckles the Professor. Then quietly he goes on to explain how to right the boat. Rupert does exactly what he is told and soon the boat is flying normally again. "I invented the gyro-chairs," the Professor explains, "because I felt it would be safer to have seats that stay right way up no matter what the boat does." With the Professor at the wheel the boat touches down some time later but as they taxi to the cave he looks concerned. "That's odd!" he says. "Where is my servant? He always comes to meet me."

RUPERT MEETS THE SPIES

Inside the cave they look around.
The little servant can't be found.

They call but no one seems to hear.
Then suddenly two boys appear.

Crossly the old man jumps ashore.
The boys stand firm, his wrath ignore.

The boys who look like pirates say
They have the servant tucked away.

The professor seems really worried. "Whenever he hears the air-boat's engine my servant comes out of the cave to meet me," he says. With its wings folded the craft glides into the cave. "Hello there!" calls the Professor. But there is no answer. Now Rupert begins to worry too. Anxiously the two get ready to jump ashore. At that moment two strange boys emerge from behind a big crate where they have been hiding. Rupert and the Professor are taken aback but the old man hops ashore, crossly demanding, "What are you doing here? Where is my servant?" Rupert can't remember seeing the Professor so angry before. But the two boys who are dressed like ragged young pirates don't seem at all worried by his crossness. Boldly they stand their ground and face the Professor. "Your servant is where you won't find him until you do as we want," declares one of the young strangers. The other boy nods his head sternly.

RUPERT MUST GO WITH THEM

*"Make us a flying-ship as well
Or where your friend is we shan't tell!"*

*"You'll fly us to our pirate lair.
What's more you'll bring that little bear!"*

*Our two are told to load with speed
The extra fuel the boat will need.*

*"Come on, let's go!" the two boys cry.
"And we'll tell you which way to fly!"*

The Professor gasps and splutters. "We mean what we say," declares the boy. After a moment the Professor asks, "And what is it I must do?" The boy gives a little smile. "Build us an air-boat like yours. But much bigger!" The Professor blinks, thinks then says, 'Very well. I see that I must." Now both boys smile. "Then you will fly with us to our island," says one. He swings round and points at Rupert. "Bring him too. We can't leave him to tell on us!"

Rupert's protests are ignored and he finds himself having to load more fuel onto the boat because, say the boys, "we have a long way to go." Exactly where or how far, they refuse to reveal just yet. At last when all is ready the Professor and Rupert take their places with the boys standing behind them. "We'll tell you the way to take when we're in the air," says the dark-haired boy. "Let's go!" And soon the air-boat is climbing away from the land.

RUPERT SEES THE PIRATE SHIP

The boys say that they're Sam and Tom
And Crossbones Isle is where they're from.

On, on they fly for many miles
Until they reach two palm-fringed isles.

Now down towards a bay they dip
Beside a tall old pirate ship.

That ancient ship could never sail.
Poor, ragged youngsters line the rail.

When the craft has reached the right height one of the boys tells the Professor which way to fly. For a long time no one speaks, then the Professor asks, "Who are you?" The dark-haired boy replies: "We're two of the Pirate Boys. I'm Tom. My mate here is Sam." The boys sound almost friendly now and Rupert risks a question: "How did you come to be pirates?" But at that moment an island appears. Near it lies a smaller island. "Crossbones Isle, ahoy!" Tom shouts.

With Tom guiding him the Professor brings the air-boat low over the island. What is waiting for them down there, Rupert wonders. Then in a bay he sees a tall old ship. "Land beside it," orders Tom. The Professor nods and eases the craft onto the calm water alongside the vessel. Rupert sees that the ship is old and shabby and that the boys lining the rail wear ragged gear. "I must say that for pirates they look awfully poor," Rupert tells himself.

RUPERT FINDS THE BOYS KIND

The Professor and Rupert find
The Pirate Boys aboard seem kind.

"We have no chairs so just sit here,"
Says Tom, "Our Captain will appear."

"The reason why we're Pirate Boys,"
Tom says, "is 'cos we have no choice."

A boy appears, he quakes with fear.
"Oh, Tom," he cries. "The Captain's here!"

As they climb aboard the pirate ship Rupert and the Professor are surrounded by Pirate Boys. They seem friendly enough, thinks Rupert as Tom and Sam lead the way to a small cabin. Tom points to a rough plank slung on ropes. "You can sit on the table," he says. "We have no chairs." "What are we waiting for?" asks the Professor. "Why, for the Captain," Tom replies. He turns to Rupert. "While we wait I'll answer your question about how we came to be Pirate Boys. It's 'cos we have no choice. Grown-up pirates kidnapped us when we were babies. They were going to hold us to ransom but the Captain lost the list of our names and addresses so they didn't know who to ask for the money. Now all the pirates except the Captain have retired and live on the small island." Just then a Pirate Boy pops his head round the door and gasps, "Quick, Tom, get 'em on deck. Captain's coming. He mustn't be made to wait!"

RUPERT IS SCARED

As on the deck they stand and wait
Tom says, "This life we boys all hate."

The clomp of feet. The whole deck shakes.
The Captain's here! Poor Rupert quakes.

The Old Professor cries, "Now you
Must let us go, my servant too!"

The Captain roars, "I'll set you free
When you've made my fortune for me!"

Rupert is still very curious about the Pirate Boys and as he and the others wait on deck for the Captain to appear he whispers to Tom, "Do you all like being pirates?" Tom glances round to make sure they can't be heard then says, "No, not really. Not that there's any real pirating to be done. Nothing but learning sea-shanties and keeping this old ship in one piece." Then everything goes quiet but for a heavy clomping and up onto the deck stumps the Pirate Captain.

He is huge and fierce and his glare terrifies Rupert. But not the Professor. "I demand that we be released immediately and that you let my servant go as well!" he bursts out. The Captain stares then roars with laughter: "Your servant wasn't taken prisoner. He was just tricked away from the cave with a message that you wanted to see him in Rocky Bay." He becomes serious: "We'll see about letting you two go after you've helped me to make a fortune."

RUPERT LEARNS WHAT IS WANTED

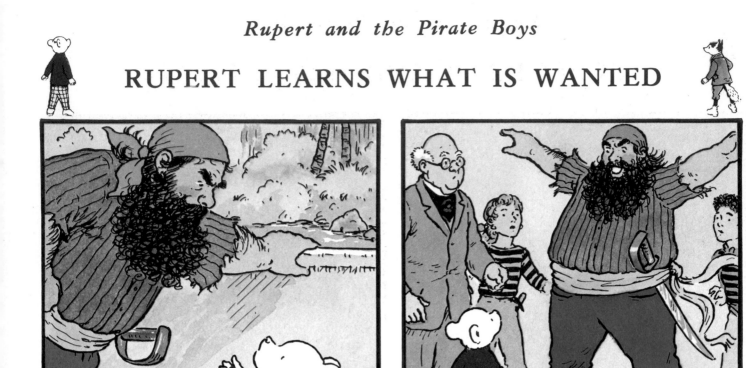

Says Rupert, "I don't understand
How we can help your pirate band."

"A flying galleon's what I need
To match the modern turn of speed."

The Captain roars, "You idle crew,
Soon there'll be pirates' work for you!"

"Tomorrow you'll start work and so
You'd better rest, so off below!"

'But how can we make a fortune for you?'' asks Rupert timidly. "By making a flying pirate ship for me!" roars the Captain. "I thought so," murmurs the Professor. But the Captain, still glaring at poor Rupert goes on, "You see, the pirating business has been very poor of late. This old galleon can't catch fast modern ships." He throws his arms wide like wings and growls, "So you and your clever old friend here shall turn it into a flying galleon ... or else! You

shall start tomorrow making me the first flying pirate, ho, ho!" Rupert doesn't answer because he is scared and the Professor because he is deep in thought. Now the Captain glares around at the Pirate Boys, "Ay, soon there'll be some real pirate work for you, idle young lubbers!" The boys mutter sullenly but fall silent under the Captain's fierce stare. "Now take the two prisoners off to bed," he orders Tom and Sam. "We shall start early tomorrow!"

RUPERT'S FRIEND HAS A PLAN

"We'd like to run away, you know,
But there's no place for us to go."

The old man who's been deep in thought
Sits up and says, "A plan I've got!"

"To show you how to fly a ship
I think that you should try a trip."

Rupert hardly knows what to think.
And then his old friend gives a wink.

When Rupert and the Professor have settled into their hammocks Tom sighs: "Now you see what the Captain's like." "Then why don't you run away?" Rupert asks. "We've all thought of it," Tom replies. "But we've no place to go 'cos we don't know who we are." He pauses then says, "Sometimes I feel the Captain does have that list of our names but keeps us as unpaid pirates 'cos all his men have retired." Just then the Professor sits up. "I have a plan," he announces.

But he will say no more about it and when they go on deck next morning Rupert is none the wiser. The Captain is waiting for them. Before he can speak the Professor begins, "You know, you should really have a ride in my air-boat to get an idea of what can be done for your galleon." The Captain considers. "Good," he grunts. "We shall go now. You too, young bear." As they climb over the side of the ship Rupert catches the Professor's eye. He smiles and winks.

83

RUPERT IS PUZZLED

The Captain says, "I really feel
The little bear should take the wheel."

The pirate growls, "No tricks, I say."
The boat takes off. They're on their way.

Poor Rupert wishes that he knew
Just what he is supposed to do.

His old friend asks, "Do you recall
The first time that you flew, at all?"

Plainly the Professor has something in mind but what it might be Rupert can't imagine. As they settle into the air-boat the Captain growls, "The little bear shall drive. Just in case you are up to something. You can tell him what to do." So Rupert takes the driving seat and the Captain stands behind him with his sword drawn. Quietly the Professor reminds Rupert how to fly the boat and soon they are lifting from the bay and away over the palm trees.

Rupert wishes desperately that he knew what the Professor plans. But he gets no hint. His friend goes on quietly telling him how to make the craft swoop, climb and turn. Rupert manages well enough but he does wish the Captain wasn't looming behind him. Then the Professor nudges Rupert and asks, "Do you recall when first you flew the boat? "Oh, but I . . ." Rupert begins, remembering how he turned the boat upside-down. "Sh-sh!" the Professor hisses urgently.

RUPERT FLIES UPSIDE DOWN

Rupert recalls with puzzled frown,
He turned the vessel upside-down.

Ah, now he sees the plan quite plain.
He has to do the same again.

The Captain cries out in alarm,
"Look out or we shall come to harm!"

Just when it seems they've gone too low
He pulls the wheel. Over they go!

Why on earth is the Professor reminding him of that first flight, Rupert wonders. Then, to his amazement, his friend says, "I'd like you to do the same again." Rupert's gasp makes the Captain ask, "What's going on?" "I just want you to see what the air-boat can really do," the Professor assures him. He snaps his safety belt into place and motions Rupert to do the same. Then, "Hold tight!" he cries. "Now, Rupert!" Rupert puts the boat into a steep dive.

"Hey, stop, stop!" howls the Captain as the air-boat swoops towards the sea. "Look out! You'll crash us!" "No, keep diving!" urges the Professor. Rupert keeps the nose of the craft pointed at the waves. Even he is beginning to be frightened when at last the Professor says, "Pull back and o-over we go!" Rupert and the Professor remain upright in their gyro-seats as the craft turns upside-down, but the Captain has to drop his sword and grab the handrail.

RUPERT'S FRIEND GETS A LIST

The Captain makes an awful noise.
He swears he has no list of boys.

They'll fly like this to Rocky Bay
If he does not do what they say.

The list (here taken out with tongs)
Tells where each Pirate Boy belongs.

Each boy's true name the paper gives
Also where each one's family lives.

The Captain howls miserably as he dangles from the handrail. "Get me out of this!" he screams. "Of course," smiles the Professor. "But first you must do something—hand over the list of names and addresses of the Pirate Boys!" For a moment the pirate forgets how scared he is. "Haven't got it," he snarls. "Lost it years ago." The Professor winks at Rupert. "Then we may as well fly back to Rocky Bay, though I don't think the Captain can hang on 'til then."

"I give in," moans the Captain. "The list's in my pocket. I can't reach it like this. Pull me in." "I don't think so," the Professor says. "I have a feeling you might change your mind once you were safe. Just hang on." From his jacket he produces a pair of extending tongs he uses in his workshop. Chuckling, he reaches into the Captain's pocket and plucks out a piece of paper. He scans it keenly. "Yes, just as I thought, you old rascal," he says.

RUPERT RETURNS TO ROCKY BAY

"Head for that island over there,"
His old friend tells the little bear.

The Captain's flown across the sea
And then dumped safely in a tree.

Gleefully round the list they throng
To find out where they all belong.

The little servant's waiting when
Our heroes get back home again.

"Now that we have the list the Pirate Boys will be able to go home," chuckles the Professor. "But what about me?" moans the Captain. "Ah, yes," beams the Professor. "You shall join the other old pirates. Please, Rupert, head for the little island over there." Rupert turns the craft back over the pirate ship lined with cheering boys. He isn't sure what the Professor means to do, then as they cross a clump of bushy palms the Professor jerks the speed control. The boat

shudders and the pirate is dumped safely into the leaves. Back aboard the pirate ship the boys are delighted when the Professor shows them who they are and where they come from. "Rupert and I will hurry home and send a boat to collect you," he tells them. Then Rupert and he set off once more for Rocky Bay. As their craft settles on the water near the Professor's cave his servant waves happily from the shore. "Oh, what a start to my holiday this has been!" laughs Rupert.

RUPERT and the

Rupert has climbed up to the crest
And near the old mill stops to rest.

It is the sort of crisp, sunny morning Rupert loves. There is no school today and he has gone exploring on the ridge behind Nutwood. When he stops to catch his breath after a steep climb he sees that he is near the old windmill. It hasn't been used for years, not since the miller built a bigger mill nearer the village. And that is why Rupert jumps up in amazement when suddenly the mill's sails start to turn.

But look! The sails are racing round.
It seems the mill might leave the ground.

What's happening? What's this about?
Rupert runs over to find out.

Rupert stares. The mill is bouncing up and down on the post that runs up the middle of it. "It's not supposed to be able to work!" Rupert gasps as the old structure bounces as if it were about to take off. "Oh, I must see what this is all about!" And off he dashes along the ridge to where the mill is rocking and swaying as its sails turn ever faster. Then as he runs up the slope towards the mill it stops.

He soon gets to it but by then
The mill's its old still self again.

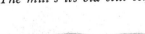

John Harrold

RUPERT TELLS HIS PALS

"Is anyone in there?" he cries.
The door stays shut. No one replies.

There's something here that is not right.
He feels someone has him in sight.

His chums look up at Rupert's yell
And wonder what he has to tell.

The windmill doesn't move a bit.
The chums think he imagined it.

The mill is so quiet again that for a moment Rupert wonders if he really did see it moving. "Of course, I did," he says aloud. "And since it couldn't start by itself someone must be inside it." He stares up at it. "Hello!" he shouts. "Anyone there?" The only answer is the sighing of the wind. Uneasily Rupert climbs to the mill door and calls again. No answer. The door is locked. But as he turns away he feels that someone in the windmill is watching him.

On Nutwood common Bill Badger, Algy Pug and Willie Mouse are playing football. But they stop when Rupert runs up and blurts out his story about the mill. "I'm sure someone's in there," he ends. "The wind must have made the sails start up," Bill says. And Willie adds, "Maybe you just imagined someone in there." "Then why don't we go and have a look," Algy suggests. So sometime later the pals arrive at the mill. It looks exactly as usual.

RUPERT'S PALS HIDE

Says Willie, "It won't move, I fear
While all of us are standing here."

They all agree with Willie so
The four of them pretend to go.

Pretending not to care they stride
Away then find a place to hide.

They wait what seems like ages then
The mill begins to move again.

Cautiously the four pals approach the windmill. They circle it slowly looking for anything at all unusual. Algy is the first to speak. "It looks the way it's looked for ages," he says. Bill and he look at Rupert as if they feel he may have been pulling their legs. "Oh, I did see it moving!" protests Rupert who can see what they are thinking. Then Willie pipes up, "Maybe it won't do anything while we're all standing here. Let's pretend to go away."

So off tramp the pals trying to look as if windmills were the last things in their minds. But as soon as they reach a bushy hollow they stop and hide. As they crouch there Willie whispers to Rupert, "A moment ago I felt the way you did, that someone was watching me from the mill." For a long time nothing happens then just when they are thinking of giving up Bill cries, "Look, it's working again, Rupert, just the way you said it did!"

RUPERT IS PROVED RIGHT

The mill begins to bounce and dance.
"Hurry!" cries Rupert. "Now's our chance."

Then when they're almost at the top
The mill slows down. It's going to stop.

"So there," says Rupert, "Now you know
That what I said I saw was so."

The other chums swing round and stare
As Willie cries, "There's someone there!"

The pals gape as the sails of the windmill spin faster and faster and the building bounces up and down on its post. "Come on!" Rupert cries, and jumps to his feet. And off he dashes to the mill with the others close behind. "I say, it's going to take off!" gasps Bill as for a moment the mill bounces quite clear of its post. But it settles back again and by the time the chums reach the crest of the ridge where it stands it has almost stopped once more. But now they have all seen it working. "There! You see I was right!" crows Rupert. And all four of them go round the mill calling out things like, "We know you're in there!" and "Why don't you open up?" and "Who are you?" Then Willie who has started up the steps to the door squeaks, "Look! There's someone at the window!" The others dash to the little mouse and stare up at where he is pointing. Behind a grimy window a shape of someone—or something—can be seen.

RUPERT IS INVITED INSIDE

They all gaze up. A window creaks.
"Oh, look it's Bingo!" Willie squeaks.

"Oh, well," says Bingo, "now I'm found
You lot may just as well look round."

"I've done my best, I should explain,
To make this old mill work again."

The whole thing really has been fun,
Though quite a lot still must be done.

The pals hold their breath. All eyes are on the window. It creaks open ... "Bingo!" Rupert and the others shout as their chum Bingo, the clever pup, sticks his head out. "I might have known you lot wouldn't give up as easily once you got curious," he chuckles. "What's it all about?" "What are you up to?" the questions tumble out from the pals. "Hey, just a second!" pleads Bingo and disappears to emerge a moment later at the door. "You'd better come in **and** have

a look," he says. Agog, the others follow Bingo into the mill. "It has been standing here doing nothing for ages," Bingo explains, "so I decided to see if I could get it going again. As you can see I've got the sails working." "What's this?" asks Algy examining a stout pillar in the middle of the floor. "That's the post the mill turns on," Bingo says. "It seems a bit loose on its post," remarks Rupert. "Yes, I'll fix it," Bingo says leading the way upstairs.

RUPERT IS TOO LATE TO HELP

"What's this?" A rope's caught Willie's eye.
He doesn't wait for a reply.

"Hey, don't touch that for any sake!"
Cries Bingo. "That controls the brake."

Now Willie has released the brake
The mill begins to groan and shake.

Bingo leaps up in frantic hope
To stop the sails. He snaps the rope.

They stop in a room full of the mill's old machinery. "You know, the mill almost took off while we were watching it," Rupert says. "Yes, that's because I still have to fix the post and this thing that stops the sails turning too fast," Bingo replies. He points to a chain hanging from the ceiling. He is just about to explain how it works when Willie squeaks, "What's this?" and unhitches a rope from the wall. "No, don't!" Bingo yells. "That's the brake!" But too late.

Willie has let go of the rope. At the same moment there comes a great groaning and whirring. The mill begins to shake so much that the pals can hardly stand. "The sails have started to turn again!" Bingo cries as he tugs on the brake rope. "Give me a hand, quick!" But before Rupert can cross the heaving floor Bingo gives a cry and falls flat on his back. The brake rope has snapped. And now the sails are turning faster and faster.

RUPERT IS STARTLED

"This brake-rope thing I must repair!"
Cries Bingo, rushing for the stair.

Then, sudden as a thunderbolt,
The windmill gives a mighty jolt.

How strange! Although the shaking ends,
The shaft still turns, observe the friends.

Now Rupert crosses to look out.
"Oh, no!" He gives a frightened shout.

The pals stare at each other in dismay as the mill judders and shakes and the squeal of the turning sails grows faster and louder. Rupert can feel the floor beginning to pitch and sway. Bingo manages to scramble to his feet. He gathers the brake rope and starts for the stairs. "I must try to fix this rope to the brake again," he cries. "Come on, Rupert. Give me a hand!" Rupert is about to follow when the mill gives a mighty lurch, throwing everyone flat.

For what seems ages the mill shakes and heaves and creaks and groans while the chums sprawl helplessly on the floor. Then just as suddenly all the movement stops. For a moment the pals are too surprised to speak. They pick themselves up. "The sails must have stopped," Algy suggests. "No, they haven't!" Bingo cries and points to the shaft joining the sails to the grindstones. It is still spinning fast. Then Rupert, who has gone to the window, cries "Oh, no!"

RUPERT FINDS THEY ARE AT SEA

The others quickly gather round.
The windmill's far above the ground.

The huge sails drive it through the air.
It's going fast—but going where?

Says Bingo, "If the sails don't slow
Then right on flying we shall go."

And now the windmill, flying free,
Goes racing out above the sea.

At Rupert's cry of horror the others rush over to the window and crowd round him. For a moment they are silent, unable to believe their eyes. Then Willie squeaks, "Oh, what have I done?" And it is no wonder the pals are horrified. The mill has jumped clear of its post and the Nutwood countryside is rushing past far below. The mill is flying! With the high wind driving its great sails it flies on and on. But going where? In fact, it is going so fast that soon the pals can't recognise the countryside below. Trying hard to sound brave Rupert asks Bingo, "Which way do you think we're going?" Bingo shakes his head. "I've no idea," he admits. "But this I do know—we won't come down until the wind drops or we can slow the sails. And since we can't do anything about the wind I'm going to have another go at fixing the brake rope." He makes for the stairs but stops and turns when Rupert gasps, "Oh, Bingo, we're over the sea!"

RUPERT HELPS BINGO

"There's just one course for us to take,"
Says Bingo. "First, let's mend the brake."

They can go down. But will they float?
They have to find a ship or boat.

"We've got to keep a look-out and
Find a vessel near which to land."

Bill at the window cries, "I say,
Here comes a ship heading this way!"

This is awful. Flying in a windmill is bad enough. But flying over the sea in one! Then Bingo speaks up: "We must try to slow the mill so that we don't get blown too far out to sea," he says, and once more makes for the stairs. "Rupert, come and give me a hand to repair the sails brake," he calls. Rupert follows and it is while he is helping Bingo that he asks, "Are we going to stop the sails and land on the sea?" "That would be too risky," Bingo says.

"We must keep a look-out for a ship." A moment later while Bingo takes a last look at the brake rope Rupert tells the others what has to be done: "Now the brake is mended we can slow the sails and even come down on the sea. But we must land near a ship or we'll be in worse trouble than ever. So everyone keep a sharp look-out for a ship." At that moment Bill who is at the window cries, "Why, there's a ship now!" Sure enough, a fast-looking vessel is making their way.

RUPERT GIVES A WARNING

"Look!" Algy cries. "Now there are two."
But Rupert thinks the first will do.

The sails are slowed. The mill descends.
Then—"Look out, Bingo!" cry his friends.

Just too late Bingo heeds the shout.
A crunch! The pals race to look out.

Two men storm out with angry threat.
Oh, dear. They do seem quite upset.

As the pals crowd to the window to see the ship Algy cries, "Look, there's another ship behind it." "It looks almost as if it's chasing the first one," pipes up Willie. "We better try to bring the mill down near the first one," Rupert says. "It will be under us in a moment." "Then shout when it's almost there," Bingo orders and clutches the brake rope. They hold their breath. "Now!" shouts Rupert. The sails slow as Bingo tugs the rope. The mill sinks gently. "Look out!"

Rupert yells. "Let go, Bingo!" Too late. There is an awful crunch and a jolt that sends the pals sprawling. Then silence. The pals pick themselves up. Rupert and Bill are first to the window. "No!" Bill groans. "Oh, no!" repeat the others when they look out. The windmill has come down slap bang in the middle of the ship's deck as neatly as if it had been built there. Nothing seems to be badly damaged. But from the ship's wheelhouse two men jump down. And they do look angry.

RUPERT OVERHEARS THE MEN

The men turn back. The five pals hear
One say the Customs boat's too near.

"If they are scared of Customs men
Those sailors there are smugglers then!"

The smugglers' boat begins to race
Towards their secret hiding place.

And even with the mill, they find,
They leave the Customs boat behind.

"Oh, dear, what do you think they're going to do?" quavers Rupert staring at the men. Whatever it is, it plainly isn't going to be pleasant for the pals. But suddenly one of the men stops and calls after the other, "We mustn't waste time on them youngsters. We can still get away from the Customs boat. It ain't far to our secret cove." And with that they scramble back into the wheelhouse. "Did you hear that?" breathes Rupert. "If they're running away from a Customs boat they must be smugglers!" The pals stare at each other in dismay. To have landed on of all things a smuggler's boat! Then the boat's engines give a great roar and the windmill sways as the craft surges towards the coast. "Maybe the Customs boat will catch them and save us," Willie says in a trembly voice. They look out at the pursuing Customs boat. It is moving fast. But not fast enough. "It will never catch up in time," Bill whispers to Rupert.

RUPERT HAS THE ANSWER

They won't be rescued now, they fear.
Then Rupert has a bright idea.

The others are quite startled when
Rupert lets go the brake again.

Once more the sails are spinning free
And drag the boat back out to sea.

Rupert's delight turns to alarm.
It's plain the smugglers mean them harm.

The coast—and the smugglers' secret cove—get nearer and nearer as the powerful craft with the windmill on board cuts through the waves. Glumly the chums watch the Customs boat drop further and further behind. "It's hopeless," groans Algy. "This boat's just too powerful." Willie wrings his hands and wails, "What's going to happen to us when they get us ashore?" But Rupert says nothing. He is thinking hard. Suddenly his face lights up and he darts over to the brake rope for the mill's sails. "Hey, what are you up to?" Bingo cries as Rupert unhitches it and the sails begin to creak into action. "Don't you see?" Rupert laughs. "The wind blew the windmill out to sea . . ." "And it will blow us and this boat out to sea again too?" Bingo finishes for him. They feel the vessel slow, stop and then start moving backwards. At the same moment from the deck come screams of rage from two angry smugglers.